Year 3 - Independent Writing

Introduction

This book of 'Independent Writing Activities' covers the genres for the 7 to 8 year old age group. It has been written to the UK National Strategy Primary Framework for Literacy.

It contains at least two independent writing activities for each genre type and is an ideal vehicle for assessing pupil progress in writing when used with the different Levels found in the Writing Assessment Guidelines, which accompany the Primary Framework for Literacy. (The appropriate levels for this age group have been reproduced under licence at the beginning of this book.)

The author has also used this approach successfully with children to embed the features of each genre. This was achieved by re-visiting a previously studied genre later in the term, so that the children practised it once again. This ensured that the features of that particular type of writing remained firmly embedded in the children's memory. Thus when the children were tested or came to write in that particular genre at a later date it was not just a distant memory.

There are six similar books in this series covering the work of pupils from Year 1 through to Year 6 (ages 5 to 11). PDF or Download versions are also available of these books for use on Interactive Whiteboards.

Index

Topical Resources publishes a range of Educational Materials for use in Primary Schools and Pre-School Nurseries and Playgroups.

Copyright © 2009 Heather Bell
First Published September 2009.
ISBN: 978-1-907269-03-5

Illustrated by John Hutchinson, Art Works, Fairhaven, 69 Worden Lane, Leyland, Preston

Designed by Paul Sealey, PS3 Creative, 3 Wentworth Drive, Thornton, Lancashire.

Printed in the UK for 'Topical Resources' by T. Snape and Co Ltd., Boltons Court, Preston, Lancashire.

For the latest catalogue
Tel 01772 863158
Fax 01772 866153
email: sales@topical-resources.co.uk

Visit our Website at:
www.topical-resources.co.uk

Writing assessment guidelines: levels 1 and 2

Pupil name   Class/Group   Date

	AF5 – vary sentences for clarity, purpose and effect	AF6 – write with technical accuracy of syntax and punctuation in phrases, clauses and sentences	AF3 – organise and present whole texts effectively, sequencing and structuring information, ideas and events	AF4 – construct paragraphs and use cohesion within and between paragraphs	AF1 – write imaginative, interesting and thoughtful texts	AF2 – produce texts which are appropriate to task, reader and purpose	AF7 – select appropriate and effective vocabulary	AF8 – use correct spelling	*Handwriting and presentation*
Level 2	**In some forms of writing:** <ul><li>some variation in sentence openings, *e.g. not always starting with name or pronoun*</li><li>mainly simple sentences with *and* used to connect clauses</li><li>past and present tense generally consistent</li></ul>	**In some forms of writing:** <ul><li>clause structure mostly grammatically correct</li><li>sentence demarcation with capital letters and full stops usually accurate</li><li>some accurate use of question and exclamation marks, and commas in lists</li></ul>	**In some forms of writing:** <ul><li>some basic sequencing of ideas or material, *e.g. time-related words or phrases, line breaks, headings, numbers*</li><li>openings and/or closings sometimes signalled</li></ul>	**In some forms of writing:** <ul><li>ideas in sections grouped by content, some linking by simple pronouns</li></ul>	**In some forms of writing:** <ul><li>mostly relevant ideas and content, sometimes repetitive or sparse</li><li>some apt word choices create interest</li><li>brief comments, questions about events or actions suggest viewpoint</li></ul>	**In some forms of writing:** <ul><li>some basic purpose established, *e.g. main features of story, report*</li><li>some appropriate features of the given form used</li><li>some attempts to adopt appropriate style</li></ul>	**In some forms of writing:** <ul><li>simple, often speech-like vocabulary conveys relevant meanings</li><li>some adventurous word choices, *e.g. opportune use of new vocabulary*</li></ul>	**In some forms of writing:** <ul><li>usually correct spelling of:<ul><li>high frequency grammatical function words</li><li>common single-morpheme content/lexical words</li></ul></li><li>likely errors:<ul><li>inflected endings, *e.g. past tense, plurals, adverbs*</li><li>phonetic attempts at vowel digraphs</li></ul></li></ul>	**In some forms of writing:** <ul><li>letters generally correctly shaped but inconsistencies in orientation, size and use of upper/lower case letters</li><li>clear letter formation, with ascenders and descenders distinguished, generally upper and lower case letters not mixed within words</li></ul>
Level 1	**In some writing, usually with support:** <ul><li>reliance on simple phrases and clauses</li><li>some sentence-like structures formed by chaining clauses together, *e.g. series of ideas joined by repeated use of 'and'*</li></ul>	**In some writing, usually with support:** <ul><li>mostly grammatically accurate clauses</li><li>some awareness of use of full stops and capital letters, *e.g. beginning/end of sentence*</li></ul>	**In some writing, usually with support:** <ul><li>some formulaic phrases indicate start/end of text, *e.g. once upon a time, one day, the end*</li><li>events/ideas sometimes in appropriate order, *e.g. actions listed in time sequence, items numbered*</li></ul>	**In some writing, usually with support:** <ul><li>simple connections between ideas, events, *e.g. repeated nouns, pronouns relate to main idea*</li></ul>	**In some writing, usually with support:** <ul><li>basic information and ideas conveyed through appropriate word choice, *e.g. relate to topic*</li><li>some descriptive language, *e.g. colour, size, simple emotion*</li></ul>	**In some writing, usually with support:** <ul><li>some indication of basic purpose, particular form or awareness of reader, *e.g. story, label, message*</li></ul>	**In some writing, usually with support:** <ul><li>mostly simple vocabulary</li><li>communicates meaning through repetition of key words</li></ul>	**In some writing, usually with support:** <ul><li>usually correct spelling of simple high-frequency words</li><li>phonetically plausible attempts at words with digraphs and double letters</li><li>sufficient number of recognisable words for writing to be readable, including, *e.g. use of letter names to approximate syllables and words*</li></ul>	**In some writing, usually with support:** <ul><li>most letters correctly formed and orientated</li><li>spaces between words</li><li>upper and lower case sometimes distinguished</li><li>use of ICT, *e.g. use keyboard to type own name*</li></ul>
BL									
IE									

Overall assessment (tick one box only)

Low 1	Secure 1	High 1	Low 2	Secure 2	High 2
☐	☐	☐	☐	☐	☐

QCA 00022-2009DWO-EN-01

Writing assessment guidelines: levels 2 and 3

Pupil name _____ Class/Group _____ Date _____

	AF5 – vary sentences for clarity, purpose and effect	AF6 – write with technical accuracy of syntax and punctuation in phrases, clauses and sentences	AF3 – organise and present whole texts effectively, sequencing and structuring information, ideas and events	AF4 – construct paragraphs and use cohesion within and between paragraphs	AF1 – write imaginative, interesting and thoughtful texts	AF2 – produce texts which are appropriate to task, reader and purpose	AF7 – select appropriate and effective vocabulary	AF8 – use correct spelling	Handwriting and presentation
Level 3	**In most writing** • reliance mainly on simply structured sentences, variation with support, *e.g. some complex sentences* • *and, but, so* are the most common connectives, subordination occasionally • some limited variation in use of tense and verb forms, not always secure	**In most writing** • straightforward sentences usually demarcated accurately with full stops, capital letters, question and exclamation marks • some, limited, use of speech punctuation • comma splicing evident, particularly in narrative	**In most writing** • some attempt to organise ideas with related points placed next to each other • openings and closings usually signalled • some attempt to sequence ideas or material logically	**In most writing** • some internal structure within sections of text *e.g. one-sentence paragraphs or ideas loosely organised* • within paragraphs/sections, some links between sentences, *e.g. use of pronouns or of adverbials* • movement between paragraphs/sections sometimes abrupt or disjointed	**In most writing** • some appropriate ideas and content included • some attempt to elaborate on basic information or events, *e.g. nouns expanded by simple adjectives* • attempt to adopt viewpoint, though often not maintained or inconsistent, *e.g. attitude expressed, but with little elaboration*	**In most writing** • purpose established at a general level • main features of selected form sometimes signalled to the reader • some attempts at appropriate style, with attention to reader	**In most writing** • simple, generally appropriate vocabulary used, limited in range • some words selected for effect or occasion	**In most writing** • correct spelling of some common grammatical function words common content/lexical words with more than one morpheme, including compound words • likely errors *some inflected endings, e.g. past tense, comparatives, adverbs some phonetically plausible attempts at content/lexical words*	**In most writing** • legible style, shows accurate and consistent letter formation, sometimes joined
Level 2	**In some forms of writing** • some variation in sentence openings, *e.g. not always starting with name or pronoun* • mainly simple sentences with *and* used to connect clauses • past and present tense generally consistent	**In some forms of writing** • clause structure mostly grammatically correct • sentence demarcation with capital letters and full stops usually accurate • some accurate use of question and exclamation marks, and commas in lists	**In some forms of writing** • some basic sequencing of ideas or material, *e.g. time-related words or phrases, line breaks, headings, numbers* • openings and/or closings sometimes signalled	**In some forms of writing** • ideas in sections grouped by content, some linking by simple pronouns	**In some forms of writing** • mostly relevant ideas and content, sometimes repetitive or sparse • some apt word choices create interest • brief comments, questions about events or actions suggest viewpoint	**In some forms of writing** • some basic purpose established, *e.g. main features of story, report* • some appropriate features of the given form used • some attempts to adopt appropriate style	**In some forms of writing** • simple, often speech-like vocabulary conveys relevant meanings • some adventurous word choices, *e.g. opportune use of new vocabulary*	**In some forms of writing** • usually correct spelling of high frequency grammatical function words common single morpheme content/lexical words • likely errors *inflected endings, e.g. past tense, plurals, adverbs phonetic attempts at vowel digraphs*	**In some forms of writing** • letters generally correctly shaped but inconsistencies in orientation, size and use of upper/lower case letters • clear letter formation, with ascenders and descenders distinguished, generally upper and lower case letters not mixed within words
BL									
IE									

Key: BL Below level   IE Insufficient evidence

Overall assessment (tick one box only)

Low 2	Secure 2	High 2	Low 3	Secure 3	High 3
☐	☐	☐	☐	☐	☐

QCA

© Crown copyright 2008

Writing assessment guidelines: levels 3 and 4

Pupil name   Class/Group   Date

	AF5 – vary sentences for clarity, purpose and effect	AF6 – write with technical accuracy of syntax and punctuation in phrases, clauses and sentences	AF3 – organise and present whole texts effectively, sequencing and structuring information, ideas and events	AF4 – construct paragraphs and use cohesion within and between paragraphs	AF1 – write imaginative, interesting and thoughtful texts	AF2 – produce texts which are appropriate to task, reader and purpose	AF7 – select appropriate and effective vocabulary	AF8 – use correct spelling	Handwriting and presentation
Level 4	**Across a range of writing** • some variety in length, structure or subject of sentences • use of some subordinating connectives, *e.g. if, when, because* throughout the text • some variation, generally accurate, in tense and verb forms	**Across a range of writing** • sentences demarcated accurately throughout the text, including question marks • speech marks to denote speech generally accurate, with some other speech punctuation • commas used in lists and occasionally to mark clauses, although not always accurately	**Across a range of writing** • ideas organised by clustering related points or by time sequence • ideas are organised simply with a fitting opening and closing, sometimes linked • ideas or material generally in logical sequence but overall direction of writing not always clearly signalled	**Across a range of writing** • paragraphs/sections help to organise content, *e.g. main idea usually supported or elaborated by following sentences* • within paragraphs/sections, limited range of connections between sentences, *e.g. over-use of 'also' or pronouns* • some attempts to establish simple links between paragraphs/sections not always maintained, *e.g. firstly, next*	**Across a range of writing** • relevant ideas and content chosen • some ideas and material developed in detail, *e.g. descriptions elaborated by adverbial and expanded noun phrases* • straightforward viewpoint generally established and maintained, *e.g. writing in role or maintaining a consistent stance*	**Across a range of writing** • main purpose of writing is clear but not always consistently maintained • main features of selected form are clear and appropriate to purpose • style generally appropriate to task, though awareness of reader not always sustained	**Across a range of writing** • some evidence of deliberate vocabulary choices • some expansion of general vocabulary to match topic	**Across a range of writing** • correct spelling of most common grammatical function words, including adverbs with *-ly* formation • regularly formed content/lexical words, including those with multiple morphemes • most past and present tense inflections, plurals • likely errors *homophones of some common grammatical function words* *occasional phonetically plausible spelling in content/lexical words*	
Level 3	**In most writing** • reliance mainly on simply structured sentences, variation with support, *e.g. some complex sentences* • *and, but, so* are the most common connectives, subordination occasionally • some limited variation in use of tense and verb forms, not always secure	**In most writing** • straightforward sentences usually demarcated accurately with full stops, capital letters, question and exclamation marks • some, limited, use of speech punctuation • comma splicing evident, particularly in narrative	**In most writing** • some attempt to organise ideas with related points placed next to each other • openings and closings usually signalled • some attempt to sequence ideas or material logically	**In most writing** • some internal structure within sections of text *e.g. one-sentence paragraphs or ideas loosely organised* • within paragraphs/sections, some links between sentences, *e.g. use of pronouns or of adverbials* • movement between paragraphs/sections sometimes abrupt or disjointed	**In most writing** • some appropriate ideas and content included • some attempt to elaborate on basic information or events, *e.g. nouns expanded by simple adjectives* • attempt to adopt viewpoint, though often not maintained or inconsistent, *e.g. attitude expressed, but with little elaboration*	**In most writing** • purpose established at a general level • main features of selected form sometimes signalled to the reader • some attempts at appropriate style, with attention to reader	**In most writing** • simple, generally appropriate vocabulary used, limited in range • some words selected for effect or occasion	**In most writing** • correct spelling of some common grammatical function words • common content/lexical words with more than one morpheme, including compound words • likely errors *some inflected endings, e.g. past tense, comparatives, adverbs* *some phonetically plausible attempts at content/lexical words*	**In most writing** • legible style, shows accurate and consistent letter formation, sometimes joined
BL									
IE									

Key: BL   Below level   IE   Insufficient evidence

Overall assessment (tick one box only)

Low 3	Secure 3	High 3	Low 4	Secure 4	High 4

QCA   © Crown copyright 2008

Flying Saucer

Read the following extract:

It was late evening, almost dark.

"I think I left my ball in the playground. Let's just go and get it before we go home," said Tom to Suraj.

They squeezed through the gap in the fence into the playground. It was a great safe place to kick a football round without people complaining about it hitting their cars.

"What on earth is that!" exclaimed Suraj.

A bright green light filled the sky just above the playground and it seemed to be dropping down in front of them.

"Flying saucer! It's a flying saucer!" gasped Tom.

Task

Your task is to continue the story explaining what happens when the flying saucer lands.

Name _____ **Date** _____

Flying Saucer

Opening Sentence:

What happens next?

How the story ends:

Name _____ **Date** _____

Flying Saucer

_____

_____

_____

_____

_____

_____

_____

_____

_____

_____

_____

_____

_____

_____

_____

_____

_____

_____

_____

_____

_____

_____

_____

_____

In Search of the Magic Ring

The magic ring has wonderful powers. You and your friends have been given a simple map, which shows where it can be found.

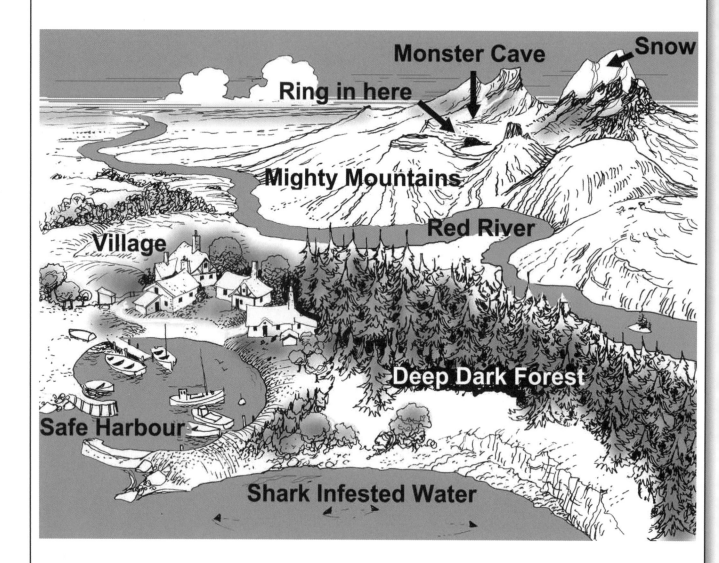

Task

Your task is to write the story of the journey from landing at Safe Harbour to finding the magic ring.

Name _____ Date _____

In Search of the Magic Ring

How the story begins:

Your journey to find the magic ring and what happens to you on the way:

How the story ends:

Name _____   **Date** _____

In Search of the Magic Ring

_____

_____

_____

_____

_____

_____

_____

_____

_____

_____

_____

_____

_____

_____

_____

_____

_____

_____

_____

_____

_____

_____

_____

_____

The Sweet Shop

Zain has been asked by his teacher to look after a new boy who has just joined his class as they live near each other. Read the passage below to find out what happens.

Zain couldn't make up his mind if he really liked Sam. He was different to Zain's other friends. As they walked down the main road which led to the estate where they lived, Zain said to Sam, "Let's go to the sweet shop."
As he spoke Sam kicked a can noisily across the pavement.
The two boys went into the shop.
"Quick! While he's not looking, put this bag of sweets in your pocket!" said Sam to Zain.

Task

Your task is to continue the story. You must decide what Zain does next.

Name _____ Date _____

The Sweet Shop

Characters:

Zain:

_____

Sam:

_____

What happens next in the story?

How does the story end?

    © **Topical Resources.** May be photocopied for classroom use only.

Name _____ **Date** _____

The Sweet Shop

_____

_____

_____

_____

_____

_____

_____

_____

_____

_____

_____

_____

_____

_____

_____

_____

_____

_____

_____

_____

_____

_____

_____

_____

Book Week

Your class are having a Book Week. They have decided to write to a famous author asking them to visit the school.

To:
John Amery,
Author,
Woodlands Farm,
Newlands Village,
Cumbria.
CA2 5UU

Task

Your task is to write a letter to the author of a book you have enjoyed, inviting him/her to come to talk to the class. Remember to tell the author about one of his/her books that you have read saying why you have enjoyed it.

Name _____ Date _____

Book Week

How will you begin your letter?

How will you end your letter?

Book you have enjoyed:

Author's name:

Characters you liked:

Parts of the book you liked best:

Name _____   Date _____

Book Week

_____

_____

_____

_____

_____

_____

_____

_____

_____

_____

_____

_____

_____

_____

_____

_____

_____

_____

_____

_____

_____

_____

_____

_____

_____

_____

_____

_____

Letter to a Friend

Think about a book you have really enjoyed.

Task

Your task is to write a letter to a friend who lives a long way away to tell them about the book you have just read. Think about the story, the characters in it, the most exciting parts and why you enjoyed it.

Name _____   **Date** _____

Letter to a Friend

How will you begin your letter?

How will you end your letter?

The name of the book you have enjoyed:

Characters in the book:

The most exciting part of the book:

Why you liked the book:

© **Topical Resources.** May be photocopied for classroom use only.

Name _____ **Date** _____

Letter to a Friend

_____

_____

_____

_____

_____

_____

_____

_____

_____

_____

_____

_____

_____

_____

_____

_____

_____

_____

_____

_____

_____

_____

_____

_____

_____

_____

_____

THE BIG WHEEL

Dominic and Molly had been taken to the fairground for Molly's birthday treat. They decide to go on the Big Wheel. Read the script below to find out what happens to them.

The children climb into their seats and the fairground attendant locks the safety bar in place. The Big Wheel starts to move.

Dominic   (excitedly) We are moving. This is brilliant!

Molly   Wow! Look at the view!

The Big Wheel takes the children to the highest point above the fairground.

Dominic   Oh, we've stopped.

Molly   (patiently) Don't worry, it will start again in a minute.

Dominic   We've been up here ages. I think we're stuck!

Task

Your task is to continue the script explaining what happens to the children and how they get back down again.

Name _____ Date _____

The Big Wheel

Characters: What are the two children like?

Dominic: _____

_____

Molly: _____

_____

What happens next?

How does the story end?

Name _____　**Date** _____

The Big Wheel

The children climb into their seats and the fairground attendant locks the safety bar in place. The Big Wheel starts to move.

Dominic　　(excitedly) We are moving. This is brilliant!

Molly　　Wow! Look at the view!

The Big Wheel takes the children to the highest point above the fairground.

Dominic　　Oh, we've stopped.

Molly　　(patiently) Don't worry, it will start again in a minute.

Dominic　　We've been up here ages. I think we're stuck!

_____

_____

_____

_____

_____

_____

_____

_____

_____

_____

_____

_____

_____

_____

The Holiday

Oliver and Amy are going on holiday with their family. Read the play script below as the children prepare for their trip.

Oliver and Amy are collecting together the things they want to take on holiday and are chatting excitedly about the trip.
The children rush into their bedroom.

Oliver   (excitedly) I'm going to put everything in this bag.
Amy   I mustn't forget Pop the Monkey or I will never get to sleep.

Task

Your task is to continue the conversation in which the children talk about the things they are going to take with them and what they are looking forward to doing.

Name _____ Date _____

The Holiday

What do the children want to take with them?

Oliver:

Amy:

What are they looking forward to doing on holiday?

Oliver:

Amy:

    © **Topical Resources.** May be photocopied for classroom use only.

Name _____   **Date** _____

The Holiday

Oliver and Amy are collecting together the things they want to take on holiday and are chatting excitedly about the trip.
The children rush into their bedroom.

Oliver   (excitedly) I'm going to put everything in this bag.

Amy   I mustn't forget Pop the Monkey or I will never get to sleep

_____

_____

_____

_____

_____

_____

_____

_____

_____

_____

_____

_____

_____

_____

_____

_____

_____

_____

Zoo Animals

Your class has just visited the Zoo. Here is a short report on one of the animals.

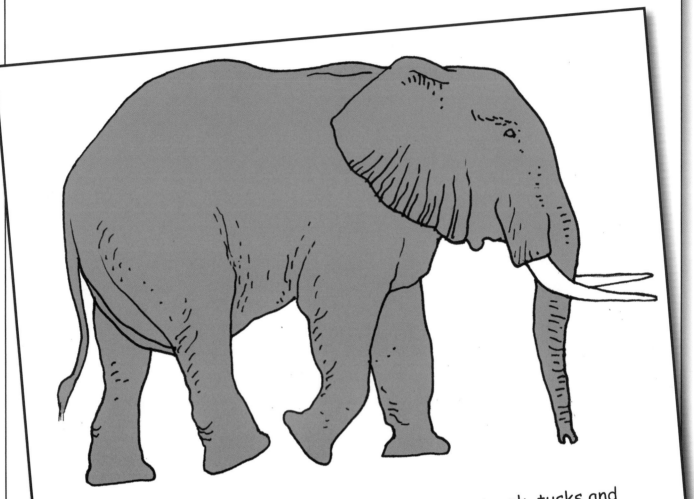

The elephant is a very big animal. It has a long trunk, tusks and large ears. It is so strong it can lift a tree trunk. An elephant feeds on large amounts of leaves, grass and bark. Elephants live in groups called herds and can live as long as eighty years!

Task

Your task is to write a report about three other creatures you saw at the zoo. (Remember it could be a fish, a bird or a reptile. You may wish to research the facts you need.)

Name _____   **Date** _____

Zoo Animals

Notes about_____

Notes about_____

Notes about_____

Name _____ Date _____

Zoo Animals

Introduction: _____

_____

_____

Information About: _____

_____

_____

_____

_____

Introduction: _____

_____

_____

Information About: _____

_____

_____

_____

_____

Introduction: _____

_____

_____

Information About: _____

_____

_____

_____

  © **Topical Resources.** May be photocopied for classroom use only.

Hobbies

Your class is making an information book about different hobbies children enjoy.

Football is a popular sport. It is enjoyed by both boys and girls. Practices are held to improve skills. Matches are played against other teams. Football kit is worn by each player.

Task

Your task is to write a report about three other hobbies. Remember it could be drama, music, art and craft or another sport.

Name _____   **Date** _____

Hobbies

Notes about:_____

Notes about:_____

Notes about:_____

Name _____   Date _____

Hobbies

Introduction: _____

_____

_____

Information About: _____

_____

_____

_____

_____

Introduction: _____

_____

_____

Information About: _____

_____

_____

_____

_____

Introduction: _____

_____

_____

Information About: _____

_____

_____

_____

How to Make My Favourite Sandwich

Think about different sandwiches.

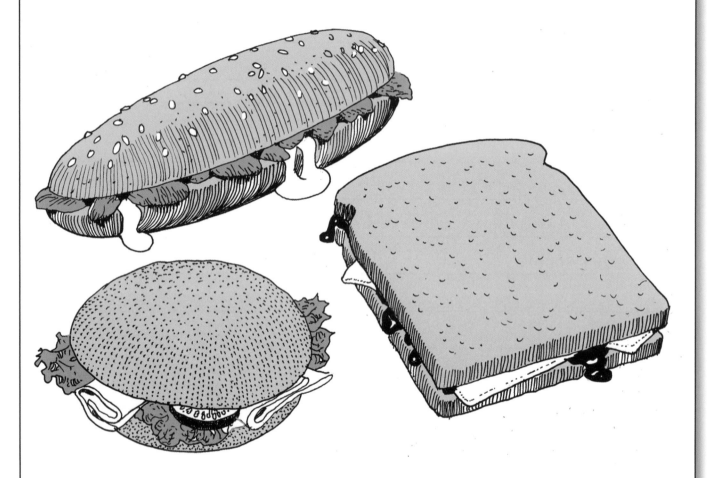

Task

Your task is to write instructions to make your favourite sandwich.

Name _____   Date _____

How to Make My Favourite Sandwich

Type
of Bread

Spread

My Favourite Sandwich

Filling

Equipment
Needed

Name _____ **Date** _____

How to Make My Favourite Sandwich

What You Need:

_____

_____

_____

_____

_____

Instructions:

1. _____

_____

_____

_____

_____

_____

_____

_____

_____

_____

_____

_____

_____

How to Play My Favourite Playground Game

Think about different playground games.

Your task is to write instructions telling how to play your favourite playground game.

Name _____ Date _____

How to Play My Favourite Playground Game

Number
of Players

Equipment
Needed

My Favourite Game

What you do

How to win

Name _____   Date _____

How to Play My Favourite Playground Game

What You Need:

_____

_____

_____

_____

_____

Instructions:

1. _____

_____

_____

_____

_____

_____

_____

_____

_____

_____

_____

_____

_____

_____

_____

_____

'Let's Party!'

Your teacher has decided, as your class has worked so well this term, to organise an end of term party. She has asked everyone to contribute their ideas about what should happen at the party.

Task

Your task is to put down your ideas in note form for the food, drink, entertainment and party games you would like to see at the event.

Name _____ Date _____

'Let's Party!'

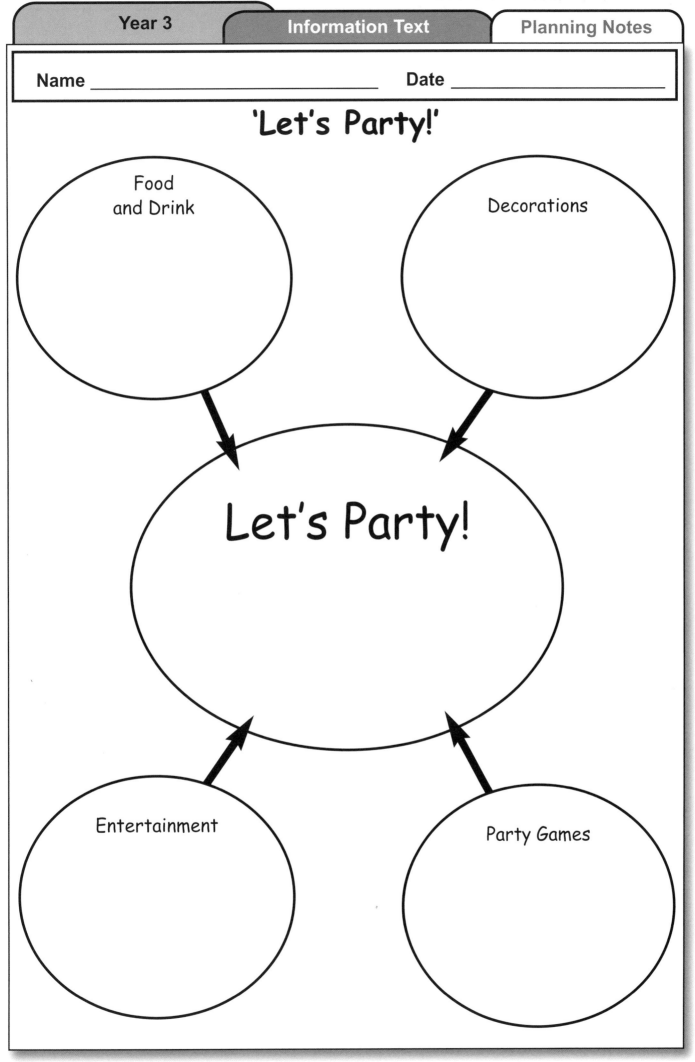

Name _____   **Date** _____

'Let's Party!' – My Notes

Food and Drink:

_____

_____

_____

_____

Decorations:

_____

_____

_____

_____

Entertainment:

_____

_____

_____

_____

Party Games:

_____

_____

_____

_____

Letter to Father Christmas

On the following page are the notes that the twins Anna and Tom made before writing their letters to Father Christmas.

Task

Your task is to write a letter to Father Christmas using the notes the twins made. The letter could be from either Anna or Tom.

Name _____   Date _____

Letter to Father Christmas

Anna's Notes	Tom's Notes
Painting Set	Train Set
Jacqueline Wilson book	Horrid Henry book
Football	Cricket Bat
Computer Game	Camera
Pencil Case	Set of Drums
Coloured Pencils	Roller Boots
Scissors	Lego Set
Glue	Bike
Coloured Paper	Felt tip pens
Watch	Basket Ball

Name _____ **Date** _____

Letter to Father Christmas

Dear Father Christmas,

_____

_____

_____

_____

_____

_____

_____

_____

_____

_____

_____

_____

_____

_____

_____

_____

_____

_____

_____

_____

_____

_____

_____

_____

_____

Ten Little School Children

Read the beginning of the poem below:

Ten little school children standing in a line,
One caught cold, then there were nine.

Nine little school children standing near the gate,
One tripped over, then there were eight.

Task

Your task is to continue the poem until only one child is left. Remember to make your poem rhyme in the same way as above.

© **Topical Resources.** May be photocopied for classroom use only.